NICK JUNIOR 2019
A CENTUM BOOK 978-1-912707-25-6
Published in Great Britain by Centum Books Ltd.
This edition published 2018.

1 3 5 7 9 10 8 6 4 2

Centum Books Ltd, 20 Devon Square, Newton Abbot, Devon, TQ12 2HR, UK.
www.centumbooksltd.co.uk | books@centumbooksltd.co.uk

CENTUM BOOKS Limited Reg. No. 07641486.

A CIP catalogue record for this book is available from the British Library.

Printed in Italy.

nick jr.™
2019

This book belongs to:

----

centum

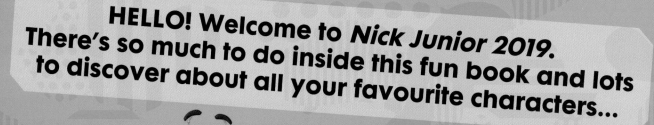

HELLO! Welcome to *Nick Junior 2019*. There's so much to do inside this fun book and lots to discover about all your favourite characters...

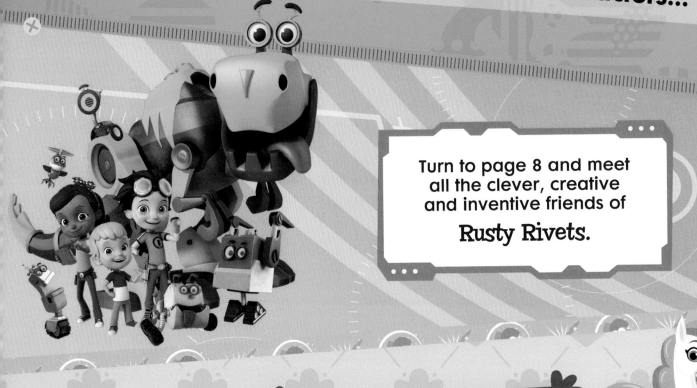

Turn to page 8 and meet all the clever, creative and inventive friends of **Rusty Rivets.**

On page 14 you'll discover lots of fun things about the brave and bold **Nella the Princess Knight** and her friends.

Start your engines and race to page 18 for lots of fun with **Blaze and the Monster Machines.**

Get ready for action
on page 38 if the
PAW Patrol
are your favourites.

Explore the
city with
Dora and friends
on page 22.

Turn to pages
35 and 36 for a fun
Nick Junior
craft to make and
pages 60 and 61 for
the answers to the
puzzles inside.

Draw you and your favourite character below.

Awesome Teamwork

Find out all about Rusty and his creative friends and team of bots.

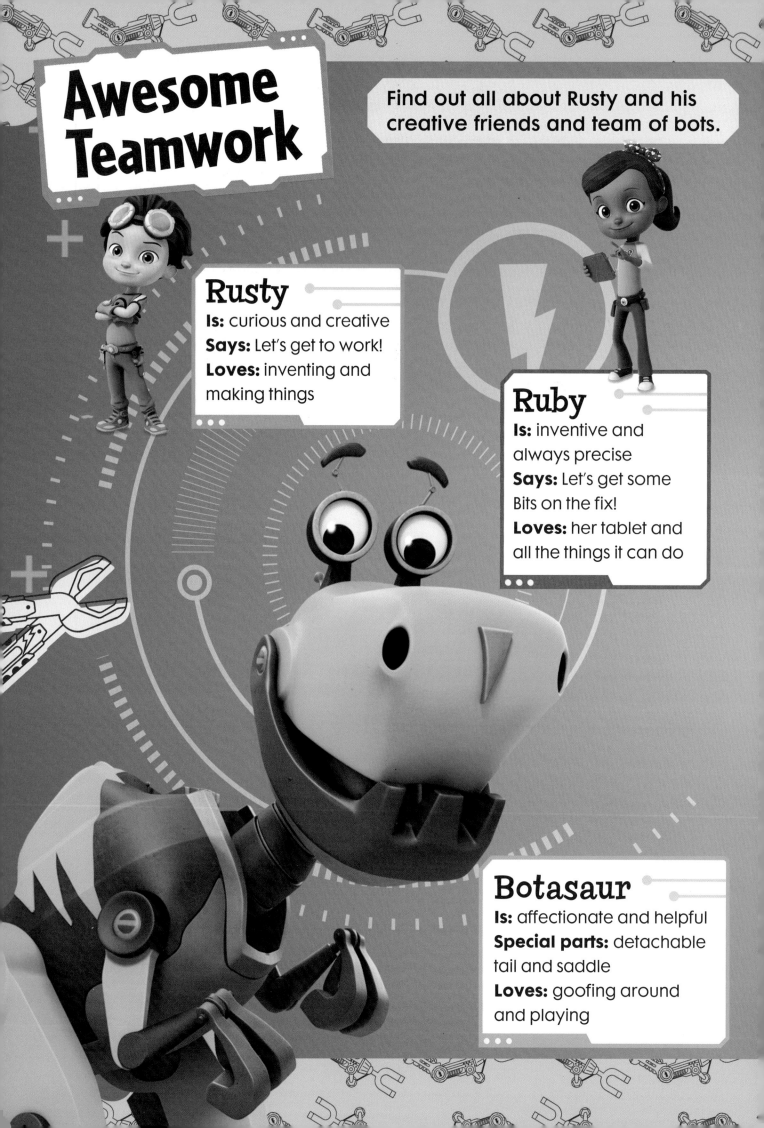

Rusty
Is: curious and creative
Says: Let's get to work!
Loves: inventing and making things

Ruby
Is: inventive and always precise
Says: Let's get some Bits on the fix!
Loves: her tablet and all the things it can do

Botasaur
Is: affectionate and helpful
Special parts: detachable tail and saddle
Loves: goofing around and playing

Whirly

Is: a bit of a daredevil
Special parts: a cool digital camera linked to Ruby's tablet
Loves: flying high and helping her friends

Liam

Is: a magnet for mayhem
Says: Well, that could have gone better
Loves: everything that Rusty does and makes

Crush

Is: eager to please and dedicated to his job
Special parts: a big powerful and steady jaw
Loves: crushing things

Ray

Is: smart and focused
Special parts: a wide-reaching spotlight and laser beam
Loves: lighting things up

Jack

Is: always ready to give his friends a boost
Special parts: a small but strong forklift
Loves: lifting things up

Which Bit is your favourite – Whirly, Crush, Ray or Jack?

Big City Friends

Can you work out which pieces go where to finish off this picture of Dora and her friends?

Dora lives in a city called Playa Verde. Where do you live?

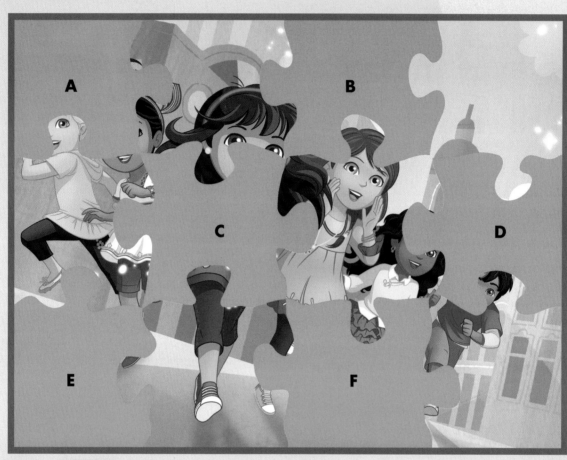

Find the answers on page 60

Perfect Pup

Can you help Ryder find the right pup to send to the rescue for the emergencies below? When you do, fill in their names into the grid.

¹M

²K

³R

⁵U

⁴E   E

1. There's a fire at city hall.
2. A scared kitten is stuck on a roof.
3. A broken bike needs fixing.
4. A huge mound of snow is blocking a tunnel.
5. A fallen tree needs to be moved off a road.

Rubble

Marshall

Rocky

Everest

Skye

Find the answers on page 60

Let's Get Knightly

Can you find 10 differences between the pictures of Nella and her friends below? Colour in the hearts when you spot them.

Find the answers on page 60

Wheely Fun

Can you help Blaze spot the odd one out in each row?

A   B   C   D   E   F

1
2
3
4
5
6

Find the answers on page 60

Heroism with Heart

Welcome to Castlehaven, home to Nella the Princess Knight and her friends and family.

Nella
Loves: being a caring princess, a fearless knight and going on adventures with her friends
Is: kind, brave and heroic

Sir Garrett
Loves: his Knightly Trading Cards and his horse Clod
Is: Nella's best friend and a brave knight

Nella's parents, the King and Queen are proud of Nella's knightly adventures.

Trinket

Loves: her friend Nella and looking her best
Is: glitzy, loyal and always on hoof to help

Sir Blaine

Loves: being the best and always winning
Is: a bit bossy and often ends up needing help

Fired Up

How quickly can you match the Monster Machine to the correct shadow?

Find the answers on page 60

Friends Forever

Can you find 5 differences in the pictures of Dora with her friends below? Tick a flower for each difference that you find.

Find the answers on page 60

Meet The Machines

Blaze

Is: a truck that can transform to save the day
Loves: to race his friends

Stripes

Is: a tiger truck
Loves: to leap and pounce

Darington

Is: a stunt truck
Loves: doing flips

AJ

Is: Blaze's driver and best friend
Loves: driving Blaze into adventure

Starla

Is: a cowgirl Monster Machine
Loves: to perform lasso tricks

Zeg

Is: a dinosaur truck
Loves: smashing and bashing

Crusher

Is: a huge truck
Loves: to cheat and beat Blaze

Pickle

Is: a speedy mini Monster Machine
Loves: everyone in Axle City especially Blaze

Gabby

Is: an amazing mechanic
Loves: using her tools to fix the trucks

Be Your Own Hero

Add some bright and bold colours to the picture below to make Nella her sparkly best.

Nella's tiara transforms into a bow, lance or sword when she's on her knightly adventures.

Now join the
dots and add
some colour
to finish this
picture too.

All For One

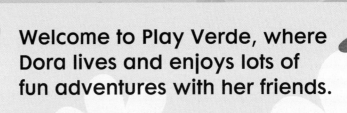

Welcome to Play Verde, where Dora lives and enjoys lots of fun adventures with her friends.

Dora

Dora loves living in the city and tries to make it a better place with the help of her friends.

Kate

Kate has a great imagination and loves to come up with stories and write plays. She's also the star of all the school shows.

Dora's adventures are always fun when she's with her friends.

Alana

Alana is a sports superstar. She also loves animals and volunteers as a helper in the animal shelter.

Emma

Emma is very musical and can play the violin and guitar. She wants everyone to love music as much as she does.

Pablo

Pablo loves sport and playing games in the park. He's always willing to lend a hand to help out his friends.

Naiya

Naiya is really smart and speaks three languages. She wants to be a scientist when she grows up.

Pup Treats

The pups are feeling hungry.
Keep doodling bones for
them till you fill the page.

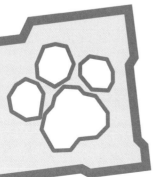

How many
did you
doodle?

24

Modified.
Customised.
Rustified.

Add some detail and doodles to help Rusty finish off his vehicle inventions.

My Heart Is Bright

Can you find Nella and her friends in the wordsearch below?

SMELGLY ♡

Tick them off when you spot them.

COACH ♡

BLAINE ♡

CLOD ♡

S	B	F	N	E	B	N	V	F	R	F	S
C	Y	U	I	E	T	U	V	O	X	R	C
L	F	R	P	O	L	V	L	M	G	F	O
O	A	G	E	K	F	L	F	V	A	G	A
D	T	W	R	Y	F	I	A	O	R	S	C
N	O	R	M	A	F	T	F	R	R	F	H
A	M	U	Q	W	E	B	A	Z	E	Z	U
E	F	F	T	K	R	G	T	U	T	T	Y
W	R	S	N	F	H	J	B	I	T	F	I
F	Q	I	F	I	F	O	P	Y	I	W	B
F	R	R	E	S	M	E	L	G	L	Y	T
T	F	N	Y	I	P	B	L	A	I	N	E

TRINKE ♡

NELLA ♡

NORMA ☑

GARRETT ♡

Find the answers on page 6

Monster Puzzles

Help Blaze work his way through the puzzles to cross the finish line.

Circle every third letter to find out what Blaze needs to get moving.

G T P L O E R S T
M N R X M O G Q L

....

What shape is Blaze's steering wheel?

Tick which item Blaze must change to help him go faster.

nd the answers on page 60

27

To The Rivet Lab

Can you fit all the names below in the grid? Then rearrange the letters in green squares to reveal what Rusty is making in the lab.

R

H

O

Y

Y

J

R

- ⊕ **BOTASAUR**
- ⊕ **BYTES**
- ⊕ **CRUSH**
- ⊕ **RUBY**
- ⊕ **JACK**
- ⊕ **RUSTY**
- ⊕ **RAY**
- ⊕ **WHIRLY**

Find the answers on page 60

Memory Muddle

Look carefully at the picture below, cover it up then circle true or false to the questions below to see what you can remember.

1. Chase is lying on top of Marshall.   TRUE FALSE
2. Rubble's hat is orange.   TRUE FALSE
3. The pups are outside the Lookout.   TRUE FALSE
4. There are five pups in the picture.   TRUE FALSE
5. Ryder is standing behind them.   TRUE FALSE

Find the answers on page 60

Charm Challenge

Can you spot the odd charm out in each row?

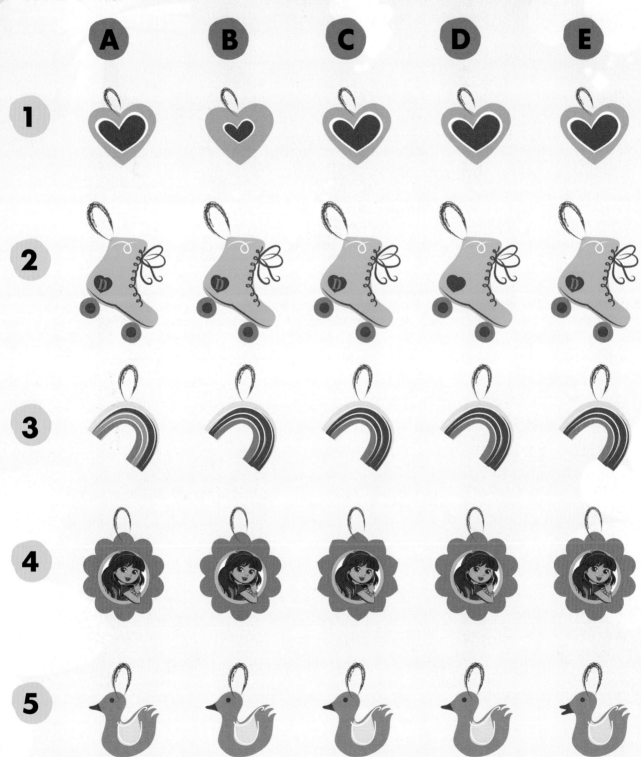

Find the answers on page 6

Let's Get To Work

Can you match these tools into pairs?

Rusty has all kinds of tools in his Rivet Lab.

1

2

3

4

5

6

7

8

ind the answers on page 60

Racing Machines

Can you find 8 differences between these pictures of Blaze racing at the Monster Dome? Colour in the tyres when you spot them.

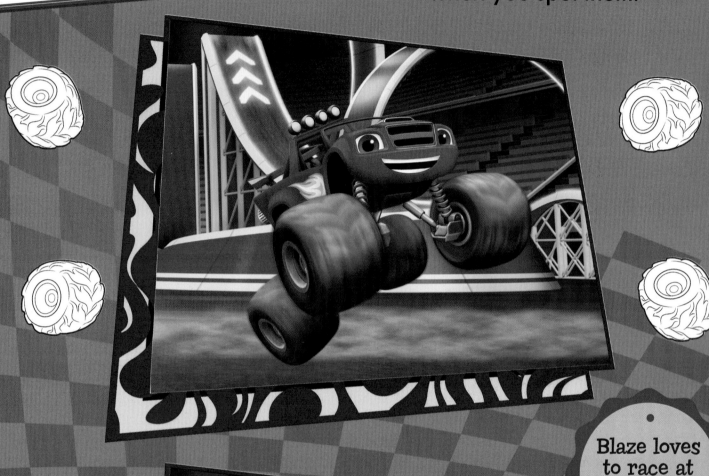

Blaze loves to race at the Monster Dome.

Find the answers on page 6

Which Way?

Oops! Rusty has lost Bytes, his robot dog. Which path should he take to find him?

Which paths lead you back to where you started?

1 2 3 4

Monster Wordsearch

Can you find Blaze and the Monster Machines in the grid below? Don't forget to look forwards, backwards and diagonally too.

DARINGTON

STARLA

ZEG

PICKLE

S	C	R	U	S	H	E	R	O	D
A	T	Q	E	A	F	I	J	U	A
K	E	A	W	E	Z	A	L	B	R
Q	P	B	R	A	D	S	O	S	I
E	J	M	Z	L	E	E	B	A	N
C	S	L	P	L	A	P	M	C	G
I	E	V	K	O	F	I	S	S	T
F	R	C	H	C	T	R	F	E	O
Y	I	P	U	J	G	T	H	S	N
P	U	G	E	Z	O	S	J	I	D

BLAZE

STRIPE

CRUSHER

Find the answers on page 6

Make & Create!

Use the template below to make a fun pen pot for your pens and pencils.

1. Cut along the dotted lines to cut out the template.

2. Add some glue where it says 'glue here'.

3. Wrap the template around a cardboard roll and press the ends firmly to stick together.

Ask a grown-up to help you cut out your pen pot template if you find it tricky.

glue here

Make & Create

Or follow the steps on page 35 and use this side of the template for a Rusty Rivets pen pot instead.

Rusty loves to get creative with his tools and friends.

© 2018 Spin Master.

glue here

To The Lookout

Oh no! The pups have got lost... help them through the maze back to the Lookout.

How many bones can you spot on the page?

Finish

Start

Find the answers on page 61

Ready For Action

Meet the heroic pups who are always ready to race to the rescue. Just yelp for help and they'll be there.

Ryder

Breed: human
Skills: a good leader
Is: brave and adventurous

Chase

Breed: German shepherd
Skills: tracking
Is: clever and always courageous

Zuma

Breed: Labrador
Skills: diving
Is: energetic and carefree

Skye

Breed: Cockapoo
Skills: flying
Is: loyal and daring

Marshall

Breed: Dalmatian
Skills: fire-fighting
Is: brave but clumsy

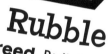

Rubble

Breed: Bulldog
Skills: digging
Is: tough but kind

Rocky

Breed: Mixed breed
Skills: recycling
Is: caring and inventive

Seek And Spot

Can you help Ryder find his team, so he can brief them for their next mission? Tick the shields below when you spot them.

Find the answers on page 61

Believe, Achieve!

Can you help Nella work out what comes next in the patterns below?

A · B · C · D · E

Find the answers on page 61

Odd Bot Out

Can you spot the odd one out in each row below?

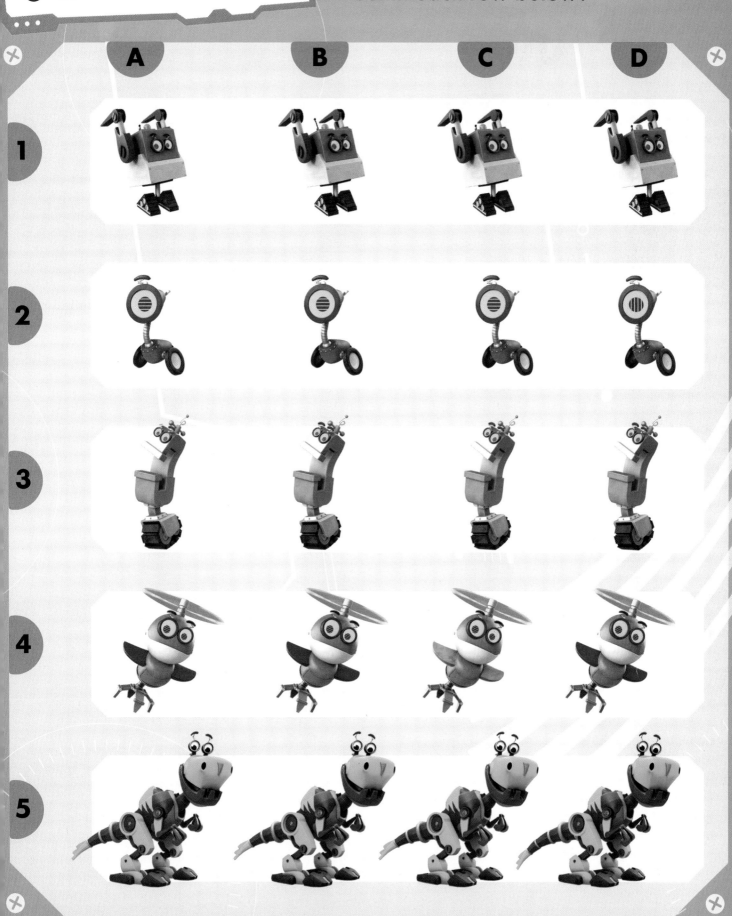

Blazing Colours

Join the dots to finish off these pictures of Blaze and his friends. Don't forget to colour them in too.

Which Monster Machine is your favourite?

Knightly Adventure

Which trail should Sir Garrett choose to reach Clod?

Which paths takes Sir Garrett right back to where he started?

Find the answers on page 61

Say It Like Dora

Learn some fun Spanish words with Dora, then fit them into the grid below.

hello = hola

play = jugar

school = escuela

friend = amigo

house = casa

let's go = vamonos

Find the answers on page 61

Customise And Colour

Now join the dots to
finish this picture too.

49

Put It Together

Can you find 8 differences between these two pictures of Rusty and his friends in the Recycling Yard?

Rusty loves exploring the Recycling Yard for parts to create his next invention.

Find the answers on page 61

Oodles Of Doodles

Keep doodling Nella's knightly doodles to fill up the page.

Say What?

Can you find the right words to finish these Paw Patrol sayings?

up

yelp

Paw

roll

deck

pup

2
Just
y
....
for help.

3
Paw Patrol,
let's ....
r

.P.............
Patrol, here
to help!

4
No job is
too big, no
p..... is too
....
small.

5
What's
.u....
pups?

6
All paws
on ....
d

Find the answers on page 61

Truck Wash

Can you help Blaze find his way to the truck wash? Try to avoid the muddy puddles along the way.

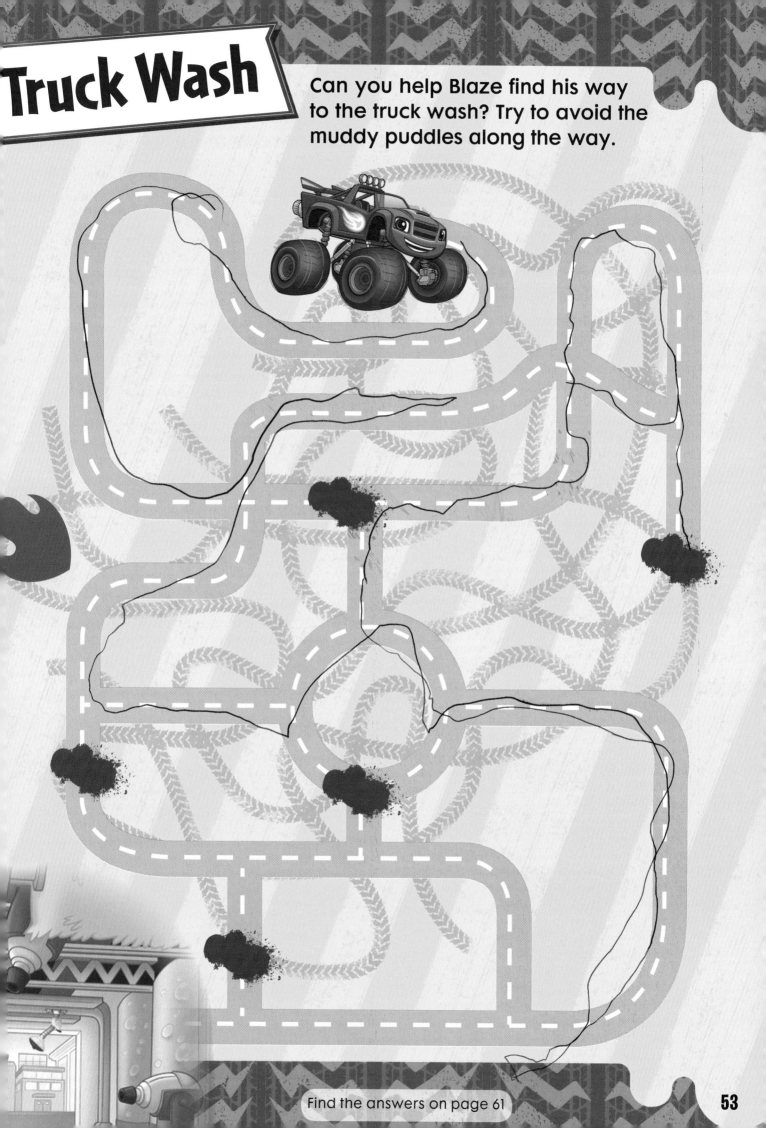

Find the answers on page 61

All Paws On Deck

Pup, pup and away!

PAW Patrol, ready to roll!

Doodle Bracelet

Use the space below to create your own charm bracelet and necklace, just like Dora's.

Monster vs Mini

Yikes! The Monster Machines tyres are in a muddle. Can you number them 1 to 10 to put them in order of size? Start with 1 for the smallest...

Find the answers on page 61

We Can Do It

Use the colour key opposite to complete these pictures of Dora and her friends.

1 black   **3** orange   **5** green   **7** pink

2 turquoise   **4** yellow   **6** brown   **8** purple

Answers

p.10
A2, B5, C1, D4, E6, F3

P.11

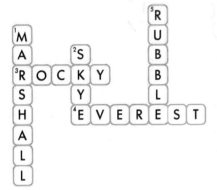

Crossword answers:
- ¹MARSHALL
- ²SKY
- ³ROCKY
- ⁴EVEREST
- ⁵RUBBLE

p.12

p.13
1F, 2B, 3E, 4D, 5C, 6A

p.16
1+7, 2+3, 4+5, 6+8

p.17

p.26

p.27

p.28

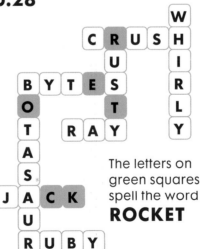

The letters on green squares spell the word **ROCKET**

p.29
1 TRUE, 2 FALSE, 3 FALSE, 4 TRUE, 5 FALSE

p.30
1B, 2D, 3A, 4C, 5E

p.31
1+4, 2+8, 3+5, 6+7

p.32

p.33
Path 3 takes Rusty to Bytes.
1 & 4 lead you back to where you started.

p.34
S C R U S H E R O D
A T Q E A F I J U A
K E A W E Z A L B R
Q P B R A D S O S I
E J M Z L E E B A N
C S L P L A P M C G
I E V K O F I S S T
F R C H C T R F E O
Y I P U J G T H S N
P U G E Z O S J I D

p.37

p.40

p.41

1A, 2C, 3B, 4E

p.42

Track C leads to the Monster Dome.

B & D lead Blaze right back to where he started.

p.43

1B, 2D, 3A, 4C, 5D

p.46

Path 2 leads Sir Garrett to Clod

1 & 4 lead right back to where he started.

p.47

p.50

p.52

1 -Paw, 2 - yelp, 3 - roll, 4 - pup, 5 b- up, 6 - deck

p.53

p.57

61